EXPEDITIONS

Scientists in the Field

EXPEDITIONS

Scientists in the Field

Science Adventures from *Nature and Science* Magazine

edited by Ruth McMullin

PUBLISHED FOR THE AMERICAN MUSEUM OF NATURAL HISTORY
The Natural History Press, Garden City, New York
1969

The Natural History Press, publisher for The American Museum of Natural History, is a division of Doubleday & Company, Inc. Directed by a joint editorial board made up of members of the staff of both the Museum and Doubleday, the Natural History Press publishes books and periodicals in all branches of the life and earth sciences, including anthropology and astronomy. The Natural History Press has its editorial offices at The American Museum of Natural History, Central Park West at Seventy-ninth Street, New York, New York 10024, and its business offices at 501 Franklin Avenue, Garden City, New York 11530.

Contents

Introduction

Is *nature* merely a world of birds and bees and flowers and trees—a "special" world that we enter or leave at will? Is *science* nothing but men in white coats—modern alchemists devoted to making "new and better" things?

A great many people still think of nature and science in these ways, even at a time when it is becoming apparent that the survival of almost all living things depends on how well we understand the processes of science and nature—and on what we do with our understanding.

We know that birds and bees and flowers and trees are all part of nature—and so are the earth and its seas of water and air, space with its planets and stars, and every living thing.

We know that everything in nature is constantly changing; we know something about the forces that cause these changes and how changes in one part of nature bring changes in other parts.

We know that science is the process of investigating nature and finding out how it works. We know that scientists of different disciplines study parts of nature from different points of view, that even non-professionals can investigate nature and its forces in an amazing variety of ways.

The six science adventure stories in this book are among the best that have appeared in *Nature and Science*. They tell of scientists of past and present as these men explore the nature of our world and try to understand it. Each voyage of exploration combines high adventure, intellectual and physical rigor—and just plain hard work. These are stories of the extensive and time-consuming plans to collect food and supplies, to hire transportation, and to accumulate scientific equipment. They also show how important it is to find the right people with the right combination of talents to go on the expeditions—people who study astronomy, geography, plant and animal life, ecology, and the very nature of human society.

Science is not just for "scientists," but for everyone who seeks to understand himself and his environment. We must learn to live with nature, rather than to "master it" or even just ignore it, if men are to survive at all.

EXPEDITIONS

Scientists in the Field

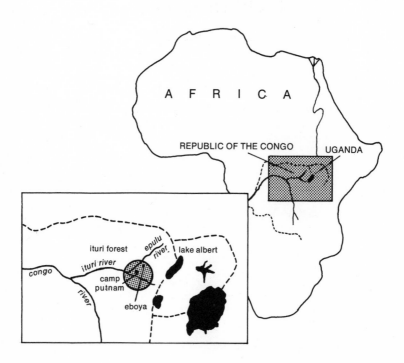

AFRICA

REPUBLIC OF THE CONGO   UGANDA

ituri forest   epulu river   lake albert

congo   ituri river

camp putnam

river

eboya

Life with the Forest People

Colin M. Turnbull

Can you imagine how it would feel to live for a year in a dense forest in Central Africa with a group of people who still live about the same way their ancestors did thousands of years ago?

This is the story of an expedition to the land of the Mbuti, a group of pygmies living in the Ituri Forest of the Congo. These pygmies grow to about four and a half feet in height. Until recent years nearly all of them lived in the forest, hunting game and gathering the roots and fruit of wild plants for food. Now, a few of the Mbuti have intermarried with other Africans and have learned to grow their own food. But the rest still live in the forest most of the time, hunting and gathering their food.

Colin M. Turnbull lived with these people at three different times for a total of about three years. Mr. Turnbull is an ethnologist (a scientist who studies the ways of living of groups of people) at The American Museum of Natural History, where he is also Associate Curator of African Ethnology.

I got interested in Africa by accident. About twenty years ago I was studying philosophy and music at a school in India. When the time came to return home to England, I decided to take a side trip and drive through Africa. Part of the trip took me along the Epulu River in the Congo.

Twenty-five years before I took this trip, two Americans, Mr. and Mrs. Patrick Putnam, had traveled to the Epulu to study the people there. They liked the area so much that they made it their home. Later the Putnams built a large mud house, and a village known as Camp Putnam grew up around it. Part of the house was made into a hospital, while another part was opened as a hotel, and the money visitors paid helped Putnam pay for hospital supplies.

When I stopped off at Camp Putnam, some pygmies were visiting there from the forest. One day I heard a pygmy woman putting her child to sleep by singing to him. The song was strange and beautiful. I didn't understand the language, but I wrote down the sounds.

When I started to sing the song, the woman became terrified. She screamed. She thought I was trying to steal the child by singing the song that she had made up for it. A lullaby is only for the person who makes it up; no other pygmy will sing that song.

Once I made the pygmies understand what I was doing, they

were happy that I was so interested in their music. After that I listened to as much of their singing as I could and wrote it down. But when I wrote down songs other than the lullabies, the pygmies didn't like it. I finally learned why. A pygmy told me that his people don't sing their best—their "real" music—when they are in the village. If I wanted to hear the real music, I would have to come with them into the forest. I did, but I didn't have nearly enough time to learn as much about the music as I wanted to. I decided that some day I would return.

Back in England, I read books about Africa. Very little had been written about pygmies, and some of what had been written seemed incorrect to me.

For example, I read that pygmy music was very simple and was almost always played on instruments instead of sung. I didn't think this was true. The European person who wrote this had lived in Africa for years, but had not spent much time with the pygmies and had not even gone with them into the forest.

This same person wrote that the pygmies were slaves to the normal-sized villagers. He said the pygmies followed the village customs and beliefs because they had few of their own. To find out whether this was true, I had to go back to the Ituri Forest.

So, I saved my money, and three years later made my trip back to Africa. I planned to stay a year.

At Camp Putnam I again met some Mbuti pygmies who said they would take me deeper into the forest. I wasn't sure what kind of food I'd be able to get in there, so I took some rice and other foods with me that would last, plus some notebooks, a few extra clothes, and a blanket. The temperature in the forest stays between 70 and 85 degrees all day, much cooler than in the open country where trees don't shield you from the sun. At night you think you'll freeze without a blanket.

I hadn't learned the Mbuti language yet. No other people speak it. But some Mbuti men know KiNgwana, a language that is used by traders in many parts of Africa. While I slowly learned Mbuti, I spoke mostly in KiNgwana.

Forest camps like this are built by Mbuti pygmies in a few hours. They hunt animals and gather vegetables nearby until they decide to move on. Their ways of living are screened by the forest and have been little known to outsiders.

It turned out that the forest is full of edible vegetables. There are so many animals that the pygmies, with their special hunting ways, have meat almost every day.

From the time I entered the forest I kept a small notebook ready at all times. Whenever anyone said anything or did anything, I wrote it down. Sometimes note-taking was very hard—for instance on a hunt, when I might have to move around very fast. At these times I would just concentrate on what was happening, and then after things quieted down I would jot down in spare moments what I remembered.

During their religious ceremonies I was embarrassed to take notes, but I did anyway. You can imagine how you would feel if you were in church during a service and someone was watching you and writing in a notebook as fast as he could. But the pygmies never seemed to mind.

At first, I worried about the dangers of the jungle, but I found that traveling in the forest is no more dangerous than anywhere else. Most animals will run away when they know a man is coming. You almost never see snakes in the forest, or any other game for that matter. You hear them, but you don't see them. I've met leopards several times, but they just look at you and go away. To get one to bite you, you would practically have to go up and step on its tail. And if you did that, things would happen so fast that you wouldn't have a chance to use a gun.

Then there are those stories about African tribes who kill people. Some of these stories are true. A herder, such as a Karamojong, who lives on the plains and raises cattle, becomes more respected if he kills someone who owns many cattle. But I had nothing to fear. I didn't own any cattle, so a herder wouldn't bother to kill me. And pygmies will not kill anyone for any reason.

Besides animals and some tribesmen, what outsiders seem to fear most about the forest is disease. Actually, the pygmies who live in the forest live longer than many people in other parts of the world. Few flies and mosquitoes are found in the deep forest, so pygmies don't often catch diseases such as malaria. The water is almost never polluted, so there is no danger from waterborne disease. If a pygmy does not die of some childhood disease, he has a good chance of living into his sixties.

I myself was sick only once—and that happened in the village at Camp Putnam. On the second day of a visit there I woke up in the morning and found that I couldn't stand. My knees wouldn't hold me. I didn't feel any pain, and all my other joints were all right. When afternoon came I still couldn't walk. Some pygmies cut sticks for me to hobble on, but I wasn't good at it. Then Mrs. Putnam drove me seventy miles to a government hospital, where doctors gave me medicine. After that my knees were all right, but for two weeks I was weak and had a high fever. I still don't know what that illness was.

After I recovered, I was able to begin my work in earnest—to learn about the pygmies and their way of life which has been hidden from outsiders for so long. The reason that so little was known about these people is that other Africans do not live in the forest itself, but in cleared areas surrounded by forest. The villagers fear the forest and spend little time in it.

Right away, I began to learn how wrong outsiders' ideas of the pygmies were. I was at a village festival called the *nkumbi*. During this festival, which lasts several months, boys about ten years old are kept in an area outside the village and go through hard, painful training that is supposed to toughen them into men. The Mbuti, whom the normal-sized villagers think of as something like servants, come to the village to take part in the nkumbi. The year I was there, no village boys were the right age for the nkumbi, so only eight pygmy boys took part. According to the sacred rules, their fathers were allowed to live in the nkumbi area with them, but

These two Mbuti are being paid in food by their villager "owner," who also supplied the clothes they wear in the village. If the villager died, these Mbuti would be expected to work for his son when they were in the village.

This photo shows Mbuti pygmies taking part in the first dance of a
sacred festival called *nkumbi,* at the village of Eboyo, about twenty-
five miles from Camp Putnam. Sabani (left), the village chief, is leading the dance. The other man with a feathered headdress is also a
villager. He is dancing in the circle with young Mbuti men who have
been initiated in earlier nkumbi. You can see a few women in the back-
ground, but they are not allowed to enter the nkumbi area.

nobody else. The pygmies and I convinced the villagers to let me stay in the area, too.

In the daytime, village men came in to lead the training of the pygmy boys. The boys had to be cut once with knives and then were made to dance and sing. They were given beds made of split logs with a rough frame over them to keep off the rain. When they ate, they could not use their hands to pick up food, but had to spear it with sticks. Their fathers were forbidden to comfort them at any time.

Each night, though, after the villagers had left the nkumbi area, the boys and their fathers ignored the rules. They got out of their beds, ate with their fingers, played, and made fun of the nkumbi and the villagers.

After the nkumbi was over and the pygmies returned to the forest, the boys were again treated as children and were not allowed to sing the parts of the pygmy songs that are for men. As far as the pygmies are concerned, the nkumbi does not "make the boys into men," as the villagers believe. The Mbuti obviously had pretended to go through the nkumbi only because they knew it would make the villagers easier to get along with but also perhaps because it helped toughen up the youngsters.

The Mbuti pygmies of the Ituri Forest in the Congo didn't mind my coming to live with them. They accepted me quickly— partly because I was willing to carry my own belongings, eat the same food they eat, and sleep on leaves or branches in the frail but comfortable homes they make from sticks and leaves.

Pygmies do not live in strict tribes in which each person is assigned to a certain job, such as hunter, fruit gatherer, or weaver. The pygmy band is just a number of families who agree to live together. There are no chiefs or medicine men or official "wise men"; each person is as important as anyone else in the band. Each adult is "mother" or "father" to all of the children, so any child may enter any house and expect to be fed and taken care of.

From earliest childhood, the pygmy's life trains him to be strong and to know the forest. At the same time, it trains him

Scars on the author's head, hands, and body were made by Mbuti friends to show that he is a "son of the forest." They cut his flesh, then rubbed in plant ashes. Mr. Turnbull is Associate Curator of African Ethnology at The American Museum of Natural History in New York City.

to work with all the other members of his band, whether they are hunting animals for food or singing complicated songs.

Whenever an Mbuti sings, he is not doing it just to please himself or the people who hear him, but also to "awaken the forest." The Mbuti think of the forest as something like a parent, who gives protection, food, and life. By singing, an Mbuti lets the forest know what he is doing or thinking about, so that the forest will help him.

Mbuti music is some of the most beautiful and complicated I have ever heard. Most of the songs are sung in a special way that we call *round* form. After a person or small group has sung a few words of a song, another person begins singing the same song, either with the same notes or in higher or lower notes. Then a third may begin singing, and so on. I have sometimes heard sixteen voices singing at once. (Two songs you may know that are sung in a simple round form are "Row, Row, Row Your Boat" and "Three Blind Mice.")

Some Mbuti songs have *solo* parts where one person alone sings the melody, but he is always accompanied by a chorus, and the solo part is always passed around so that no person sings the whole song completely alone.

Hunting songs and some others are made even more difficult by singing them in *hoquet (ho-kay)*. Each person or small group sings only one note of the song. Then a different person or group sings the next note, and so on. The singers sit or stand in a circle. As the song is passed around the circle in a clockwise direction, the same song but with different notes may be passing around counterclockwise. But always all the notes must blend together in a pleasing sound.

Singing is often accompanied by beating sticks together or hitting drums. Wooden whistles are sometimes blown, especially before a hunt.

All Mbuti men and women except the very old and the very young help in the hunt. I'll tell about one I went on.

The band went singly or in small groups to an area that had

been decided on the night before. Each of the married men and some of the older bachelors carried nets four feet high and between one hundred and three hundred feet long. While the women and children went off into the forest, the men fastened their nets together, forming a single net several thousand feet long. They hung the net on bushes and low branches until it formed a large semicircle, with the hunters on the outside. Then they waited. The forest became very quiet. Not even crickets

This Mbuti hunter will tie his net to other hunters' nets to make a giant trap for animals. Nets are made of dried vines that the Mbuti shred and weave together. An Mbuti mother will often make a complete net to give to her son when he marries.

could be heard. Suddenly from another part of the forest, shouting and clapping burst out as the women and children started to beat the underbrush.

They were about a half mile away, moving toward the net. An antelope bounded out of the bushes and ran toward the net near where I was standing, but before it reached the net it turned away. Soon there was a sound of thrashing, and I knew the antelope had been caught in another part of the net. Several pygmies near me jumped over the net and ran in that direction to help in the kill.

Now came the most dangerous part of the hunt. When animals get caught in the net, they fight. The pygmies spear them or shoot them with arrows that are tipped with a poison that can kill in less than a minute. Everyone must know what his neighbors are doing, and each person must do what is expected of him. Otherwise the hunt may not catch enough food, or someone may be hurt or killed.

A small but dangerous antelope called a *sindula* got caught in the net near where I was. A thirteen-year-old boy speared it to the ground, but it kept thrashing and kicking about. Another youth ran over and speared it through the neck, and a third speared it through the heart and killed it.

After the hunt, the meat of any animals too large to carry back was divided up on the spot. The smaller animals were thrown into baskets carried by the women. Certain parts of the animals would later be given to children and to old people—making sure that nobody went hungry.

There is a connection between the pygmies' singing and their hunting. The hunting songs are always sung in hoquet, the most difficult form to sing. For a song sung in hoquet to be "pleasing to the forest," all the singers must know their parts perfectly and sing them at exactly the right time. And if a pygmy band's hunt is to be successful, with no one getting hurt, the whole band must work together with perfect timing and knowledge of what the others are doing. A hunt has no leader, just as a song has none, but for either to be a success, everyone must work together.

I wondered why there is so much likeness between these two different and important parts of pygmy life. Perhaps singing helps teach a pygmy child the importance of working well with the other members of the band, long before he goes on his first hunt.

But sounds are important to the Mbuti in many other ways.

These Mbuti pygmies are holding tight to an antelope that is still kicking after its throat has been cut. The animal was killed after it was driven into the hunters' nets by the women and children.

Young Mbuti hunters prepare to smoke meat to take to a nearby village. If Mbuti get a lot of meat during a hunt, they often share it with villagers.

"Noise" or "bad sound" is disliked because it does not sound nice and "displeases the forest," and also because it shows no co-operation with the rest of the band. It drowns out the forest's "talk"—animal cries and the sound of trees falling, for instance, which the pygmies need to hear in order to know what is going on around them.

You may say that if the Mbuti work so well together, why don't they all sing the same notes in a song? I think it's because the Mbuti are a very free people. They don't like to be bossed or made to stay in one place or do one thing. So in their singing, each person does something different, but the different things blend together to make one pleasing piece of music. It is this blending, or co-operation, or whatever you choose to call it, that seems to be the most important thing in the life of the pygmy.

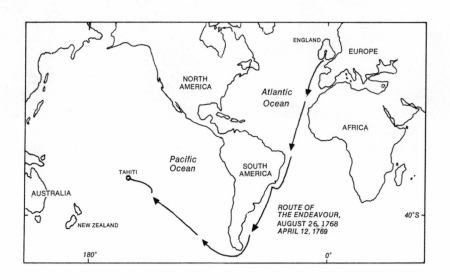

Around the World with Captain Cook

Jean Le Corbeiller

How far away is the sun?

Today, when man is terribly concerned with the moon, Captain Cook's voyage around the world may seem very distant. But is it? Some of the elements of his expedition were astronomy and surveying, a need for international co-operation, and the challenge of unknown lands.

Instead of a compound rocket, Captain Cook had a 368-ton sailing ship. He had to concern himself with the health of his crew, the stowing on board of the equipment needed to make precise measurements, and a sufficient food supply. Many of these concerns are not unlike those that astronauts and ground crews face today. In addition to astronomy and mapping, Captain Cook had to be prepared to make scientific observations on the plant and animal life in an unknown world. This, too, has parallels today.

On August 26, 1768, a small three-masted sailing ship, H.M.S. *Endeavour*, sailed out of Plymouth, England, and headed for the open Atlantic. There were ninety-four men aboard, including a party of eleven scientists. Among them was the twenty-five-year-old botanist, Joseph Banks. The ship's captain was Lieutenant James Cook, who carried secret sealed orders from the British Admiralty.

Cook's orders amounted to this: He was to sail to the island of Tahiti—in the South Pacific—by rounding the tip of South America. He was to reach Tahiti at least a month before June 3, 1769. On that date he and the members of the scientific staff were to observe a rare astronomical event—the *transit*, or passing, of the planet Venus across the sun's disk. Next, he was to sail south (as far as 40 degrees south latitude) in search of the mysterious Great Southern Continent—a huge land mass which geographers of the time thought must exist in the Southern Hemisphere. If it was not found, Cook was to sail west until he reached the unknown east coast of New Zealand. He was to explore the coasts of New Zealand as fully as possible and then return to England.

The first part of Cook's orders—observing the transit of Venus —was public knowledge. The second part—the exploration for unknown continents and islands—was what we today would call "classified." It was a secret plan of the government of young King George III—in fact (by oversight) these orders were not "declassified," or made public, till 1928.

After leaving Madeira in September 1768, the *Endeavour* crossed the Atlantic (and the equator), picked up fresh food and water at Rio de Janeiro, Brazil, and rounded Cape Horn, at the

N. Dance pinxit   *1793*   *Sculpt. apud J. S. Klauber Augusta.*

tip of South America, in January 1769—midsummer in those parts. Cook then headed for the open Pacific.

The Pacific was almost entirely unknown in Cook's time—almost as unknown as the far side of the moon is to us. Only forty years before, Jonathan Swift had been able to pack entire imaginary countries into it when he wrote *Gulliver's Travels*. In the North Pacific he had felt free to place Brobdingnag, with its giants, and the empire of the crazy scientists, known as the Balnibarbi. Southwest of Australia he could place the land of the Houyhnhnms (which some people read "winnums" and others render by neighing like a horse). And when Gulliver visited Lilliput, he was somewhere between what we today would call Tasmania (an island off the southeast lobe of Australia) and the *northern* coast of Australia! Swift could write freely about the Pacific because vast reaches of it had still never been crossed.

The British Admiralty was much interested in knowing just what lands could be found—and claimed as British territory—in these vast stretches of ocean, and was determined to find out. But first, there was the matter of the transit of Venus, which was to occur June 3, and which was very much worth observing.

Transits tie together planes of observation that are normally separate, and in so doing they also (as the English astronomer Edmund Halley had figured out two generations before) provide a way of deriving the distance from the earth to the sun. The word *transit* is simply borrowed from the Latin word for "passage." When a "transit of Venus" takes place, Venus (seen from the earth) is in transit across the face of the sun—that is, it can be watched as it crosses the sun's disk. This is an event that takes place no more than twice every 113 or 130 years. The reason it doesn't happen more often is that the earth and Venus don't lie in the same plane.

Suppose you have a large sheet of paper, lying flat on a table. You can mark a point in the middle, to stand for the sun. Around it you can draw a wide circle, which will be a close enough picture of the earth's orbit of Venus. Where do you draw it? The answer is: You can't—at least, not on the same sheet of paper. So you take another sheet, put the sun in the middle again, and draw a circle of seven tenths the diameter of the orbit you drew on the other sheet. To see how the plane of Venus cuts the plane of the earth, fit the two sheets so that they make an angle of 3½ degrees.

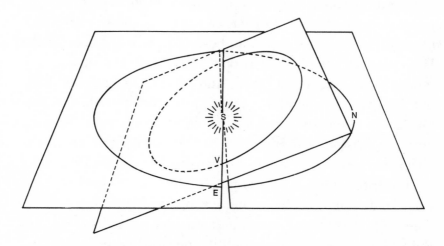

Now imagine the earth traveling around its orbit at the rate of one full circle every 365 days, and Venus completing a full circle around *its* orbit every 225 days. When will someone standing on the earth see Venus passing in front of the sun? Only when the earth and Venus happen to cross the straight line joining the two planes. When this happens, the earth, Venus, and the sun will all lie exactly in a straight line.

This is a rare event. It has been observed only in the following years:

1639
1761
1769
1874
1882

(No transits of Venus are scheduled to occur in our century. The next ones are due in 2004 and 2012).

In Cook's time astronomers the world over observed the transit of 1761 and did a poor job of it. By 1769 they were determined to do the job right. Observations were planned from Vardo (an island to the north of Finland), from St. Petersburg in Russia, from North Cape (the northernmost point of Norway), from Paris, from Greenwich, from Gibraltar, from Cambridge, Massachusetts, from Philadelphia, and from San Jose, California. And so, as the earth rotated in its regular twenty-four-hour night-and-day cycle, each team of observers would have a chance to see the transit and to time it as exactly as it could. But St. Petersburg, Philadelphia, and most of the other places that presented themselves are all in the Northern Hemisphere. What the astronomers hoped was that a few observations would come in from below the equator. Observations were already planned from Cape Town, near the southern tip of Africa, and another observation from the other side of the earth would be worth going to some trouble to get. Cook's voyage to the Pacific would thus be of great value.

Once Cook had rounded the tip of South America, he headed northwest, then westward toward Tahiti. In doing so, he sailed right across areas where map makers thought the Great Southern Continent was.

Cook had no great difficulty knowing how far north or south he was. He merely had to note how high above the horizon certain stars were at night. But knowing how far *west* he had gone was much more difficult. If you notice which stars are exactly overhead at midnight, you can tell how many degrees you have traveled west of the prime meridian, located at Greenwich, England. But during this voyage, Cook had no way of knowing exactly when midnight (or any other time) occurred.

If one had been at sea for months or weeks, the only way of telling the time would be through the ship's clock, and clocks were simply not that accurate. Since the earth turns 360 degrees in twenty-four hours, an error of ten minutes (one sixth of an hour) would mean an error in longitude of $1/6 \times 1/24 \times 360$ degrees, or 2-1/2 degrees—about 150 miles! (The most famous error in longitude, one might say, was made by Columbus when he mistook the Caribbean for Cathay!)

Until clockmakers could produce a really reliable ship's clock, navigators far from land had to estimate the time by means that seem extraordinarily devious to us today. They reasoned like this: A clock is something that turns very evenly with time. Well, the satellites of Jupiter turn around almost evenly with time and pass into Jupiter's shadow at fairly predictable intervals; the moon, also, turns evenly. So the satellites of Jupiter are really a clock— and so is the moon. In Cook's time, navigators had given up trying to tell the time by Jupiter's satellites, but they did rely on tables predicting the moon's position (which shifts 12 degrees every twenty-four hours) as seen from Greenwich. So Cook merely noted how far behind the moon seemed to be lagging and then calculated how many degrees west of Greenwich he was.

The *Endeavour* reached Tahiti on April 12, 1769, allowing the group almost two months to get ready for the transit. Cook and his party went ashore and made friends with the Tahitians. He then settled on a spot for his encampment, to this day still called Point Venus on maps. His men built a camp and surrounded it with a picket fence.

Preparations were going nicely, when an alarming discovery was made. One of the expedition's key instruments had disappeared. It was a large brass *quadrant,* a kind of protractor for measuring angles in the sky. This is how Cook (in his own spelling) recorded the catastrophe:

TUESDAY 2nd. This morning about 9 oClock when Mr. Green and I went to set up the Quadt it was not to be found, it had never been taken out of the Packing case (which was ab[ou]t 18 Inches square), sence it came from Mr. Bird the Maker, and the whole was pretty heavy, so that it was a matter of astonishment to us all how it could be taken away, as a Centinal stood the whole night within 5 yards of the door of the Tent where it was put together with several other Instruments but none of them missing but this.

H.M.S. *Endeavour*

Why had the Tahitians made off with the quadrant? They couldn't possibly have any idea of its function, but that hardly mattered. What they saw was that it was a glorious, shiny contraption made of brass. Captain Cook and Joseph Banks may have been living in the eighteenth century, but the Tahitians were still living in the Stone Age. To them, such a fine piece of worked metal was obviously magical. Cook sent out search parties, and before nightfall the quadrant had been found—slightly damaged, but one of the men on Banks' staff repaired it.

The day of the transit was a great moment for Cook. He was a man who had risen from simple seaman on a merchant ship to leader of his country's Pacific expedition. His own report—old spelling and all—reads as follows:

> SATURDAY 3rd. This day prov'd as favourable to our purpose as we could wish, not a Clowd was to be seen the whole day and the Air was perfectly clear, so that we had every advantage we could desire in Observing the whole of the passage of the Planet Venus over the Suns disk: we very distinctly saw an Atmosphere or dusky shade round the body of the Planet which very much disturbed the times of the contacts particularly the two internal ones. Dr. Solander observed as well as Mr. Green and my self, and we differ'd from one another in observing the times of the Contacts much more than could be expected.

This passage is worth a close reading. What Cook was observing (and timing) was not one event but four:

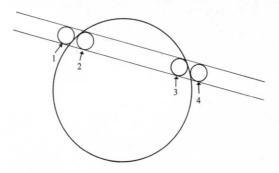

These were: the moment (1) when the disk of Venus makes its first outside contact with the disk of the sun; (2) the moment when it is tangent to the inside of the sun's disk; then, a few hours later, the moment of inside contact (3) just before Venus seems to leave the sun and (4) the last moment of outside contact.

It was these observations, sent in by Cook and other observers throughout the world, that the astronomers, back in their European observatories, would work from. They would try to figure out what proportion of the sun's disk was spanned by a reliable observation made from a point north of the earth's equator—like Vardo, north of Finland—and by an observation made from south of the equator—like Tahiti. (In our diagram, this would be the ratio of PQ to YY.)

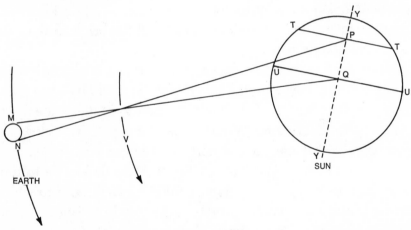

The astronomers knew the size of the earth, and they knew the ratio (not the actual mileage) of the distances EV and VS—in round numbers, it was 3 : 7. Triangles MVN and PVQ were similar, so that if MN (on the earth) was 3000 miles, PQ (on the sun) was 7000 miles. (Note: the reason the two triangles can be *considered* similar, even though they obviously are not, is that their long sides are very, very long.)

What they hoped to derive from the reports of Cook and the other observers was the diameter YY of the sun compared to the line PQ—and all the angles of the two triangles. With that they could figure out what the distance from earth to sun really is.

Cook's difficulties in observing the times of contact were not his alone. Throughout the world, some 149 other observers, at seventy-six other stations, were having exactly the same trouble: *They couldn't decide exactly when internal contact was occurring.*

The trouble is that at each moment of "contact," as Cook called it, a little bridge of black suddenly appears and joins the black disk of Venus to the vast black space around the sun. This is an optical effect.

For instance, at contact 3, just before Venus touched the sun's inside edge, a little bridge of black suddenly appeared to join the black disk of Venus to the vast black space around the sun. And neither Cook nor any of the other observers could decide at just what moment the dark disk of Venus and the bright disk of the sun were exactly touching.

Now the length of the line PQ on the sun was going to be determined by how long the two chords TT and UU were going to be, and the length of the chords (this was Halley's idea) was going to be determined by how much longer the transit would last when seen from the far north of Finland than when seen from a southern station (such as Tahiti). This difference in time was about twenty minutes. If one could time the transit to within two seconds, the accuracy would be 2 seconds out of 20×60, or 1200 seconds—an accuracy of 1 part in 600. But when the times of internal contact actually occurred, a wave of confusion passed over the earth from Kamtchatka to Tahiti: Instead of the uncertainty's being a matter of seconds, it was a matter of minutes!

As a result, the transit timings sent in by Cook and the other observers showed such wild variations that it was difficult for astronomers to draw any firm conclusions from them. Two generations later, the Berlin astronomer J. F. Encke pored over all the transit observations and, after a great deal of juggling of figures, concluded that they pointed to an earth-to-sun distance of some 95.37 million miles. This is a good figure (only 2½ per cent larger than the value used today). But when an investigator gets a sharp figure out of "soft" data, how can one be sure that he was anything more than lucky and that some appreciable errors didn't just happen to cancel out? However he came by it, Encke's figure stood as the best one available for a long time after him.

Cook's astronomical work was now over, and his exploring could begin. What the Admiralty had instructed him to do next was to check on New Zealand—specifically, how far south and east did it extend? But what was really on everyone's mind was the exciting question of the existence of a Southern Continent.

Perhaps the two questions might turn out to be different ways of asking the same thing. New Zealand's west coast (and no more) had been sighted by the Dutch explorer Abel Janszoon Tasman in 1643. If it turned out to be a vast land mass extending far to the south, then it *was* the Southern Continent. If it was merely an island, then Cook still had to push on a bit farther to see whether a Southern Continent lay to the south. So after leaving Tahiti and looking over some of the small neighboring islands, he headed westward, keeping the *Endeavour* as close to 40 degrees south as gales and high seas would let him. On October 7, 1769, Nick Young—a twelve-year-old boy—sighted land from the mast. Was this the land Tasman had seen? Cook would have to follow its shores and plot the land form on a chart.

For the next four months the *Endeavour* worked its way around most of what we now know as New Zealand's North Island. (But a modern map, with its ready-made printed outlines, doesn't give the right idea—it is better to imagine a blank stretch of ocean with Cook's shores coming into being frame by frame, as in a cartoon movie.)

Part of the time was spent in preparing detailed charts of their shores—some seventy-four hundred miles of coast line. Cook discovered the strait between the two islands. Tasman had thought that it was a bay. In a formal English ceremony that included

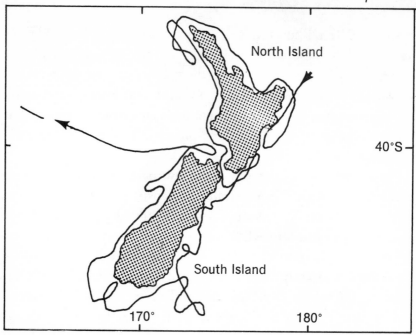

Captain Cook's route around North and South islands

setting up a marker with an inscription, hoisting the British flag, and drinking a toast to the Queen, Cook took possession of South Island (as it is now known) for the English Crown. He did all this in front of native Maori tribesmen who had gathered to watch. At the close of the ceremony Cook handed out to the tribesmen silver coins bearing the date 1763.

Cook next sailed down the east coast of South Island. (But there again, calling it South Island gives the wrong idea. Cook and his shipmates didn't know it was an island—it might be the northern tip of a Great Southern Continent.)

Before the ship had sailed very far south, several of the men on board (Banks among them) felt that since they hadn't made a complete, closed circle of North Island, they should do so. Cook turned northward again until he came to a point on the east coast of North Island that everyone remembered having seen before. They then headed southward again.

By March 10, 1770, Cook was sure that South Island was only an island and that he had reached its southernmost tip; in his diary he wrote:

> I began now to think that this was the southermost land and that we should be able to get round it by the west, for we have had a large hollow swell from the SW ever sence we had the last gale of wind from that quarter which makes me think that there is no land in that direction.

The ancestors of these Maoris may have performed the traditional poi dance in similar costumes for Captain Cook.

He was right. He next took the *Endeavour* northward along the west coast of South Island, returning to the strait, today known as Cook Strait.

Cook had carried out his orders and was now free to return home. His party had by this time been away for more than a year and a half. He decided to return to England by the Cape of Good Hope, the southern tip of Africa. This would allow him to refit his ship at Batavia (renamed Jakarta on recent maps). It would also put him within reach of the eastern coast of Australia, which he decided to explore before returning home.

Although the Dutch had explored much of the coast of Australia, no one knew just where its eastern edge lay or what its landscape was like. And not one of the navigators who had been anywhere near the area had been able to find out. By the time they had reached these remote waters, rot and shipworms (which bore into the wooden hull) had crippled their ships and the crews were down with scurvy, a disease caused by the lack of certain foods. But Cook knew how to take care of his ship. Although an understanding of vitamins was still 150 years away, Cook's insistence on fresh meat and vegetables for the crew had paid off handsomely. The *Endeavour* had not lost a single man through scurvy.

Cook set off for Australia, and after three weeks found himself near the southern tip of Australia's eastern shore. Because he had only three or four months' food supply on board, he decided to sail northward along the coast without stopping to explore every inlet. He did go ashore for water, however, and had a few brief run-ins with the Australian aborigines—"Indians" to the crew. He had no difficulties in navigating until he had sailed about halfway up the coast; then he fell into a trap he could not possibly have foreseen.

Lying almost two hundred miles offshore—much farther out than the *Endeavour's* course—was the Great Barrier Reef. Its coral barricades lay almost parallel to the Queensland shore but inched closer and closer landward toward the north. It was like

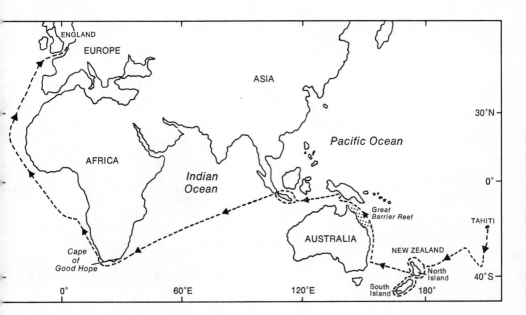

sailing into the mouth of a long V. On June 10 the *Endeavour* rammed a coral reef, poking gaping holes in her side. Water rushed in so fast that the men working the pumps could barely take care of it. The ship was refloated on the rising tide and temporary repairs were made. The ship would have gone down if a large chunk of coral had not broken off and remained stuck in the hole when the ship floated free. The coral had served as a plug. Cook now had to find a harbor in order to repair the ship properly. The mouth of a river, now known as the Endeavour River, was chosen.

It took the carpenters six weeks to patch up the ship's hull. During that time the rest of the ship's company explored the Queensland countryside. The plants were of interest only to Banks and his associates, and the natives were difficult to fathom. The one local offering that everyone could appreciate was the kangaroo. "What to liken him to I could not tell," Banks wrote in his journal, "nothing certainly that I have seen at all resembles

This engraving made in 1773 shows the *Endeavour* beached for repairs on the coast of Australia after the ship had rammed into a coral reef. While the carpenters worked, the rest of the ship's company explored the countryside.

him." After several fruitless chases (even Banks's greyhounds couldn't keep up with the kangaroos), the explorers shot one weighing eighty-four pounds. They examined it closely.

Banks was more and more puzzled: "To compare it to any European animal would be impossible..." Under Banks's remark lay a truth that none of his generation had any idea of: The kangaroo is a marsupial, and there isn't a single marsupial on the whole continent of Eurasia (the only one in North America is the opossum). Compared to most mammals, marsupials are at a disadvantage before birth in that their environment and nutrition are not controlled by a placenta; after birth, on the other hand, they have the comfort and protection of the mother's pouch.

Sydney Parkinson, one of the artists in Banks's retinue, made two drawings of the kangaroo—the first drawings of a kangaroo by a European. Parkinson meant to do a painting of the kangaroo but died of malaria before he had the opportunity. Fortunately,

Kangaroos were "new" animals to Cook's men. One of the men drew sketches from which this engraving was made in 1773.

Banks brought home two skins and two skulls, and the English painter George Stubbs (better known for his paintings of horses) worked from these when he painted a kangaroo for Banks in 1773. Later, many European pictures of kangaroos were merely copies of engravings inspired by Stubbs's painting.

On August 4, nearly two months after the wreck, the *Endeavour* set sail again. A few weeks later, she reached the northern tip of Queensland. As Cook had hoped, open water now appeared to the west—there was a strait between Australia and New Guinea, Torres Strait. Cook reached Batavia in October, and thorough repairs of the ship were now made. It was during this time—ten weeks—that Cook suffered his greatest loss: More than thirty of his men died of malaria or dysentery.

By March 1771, the *Endeavour* was in Cape Town, at the tip of South Africa. In his journal Cook notes that "the Cape lies in 34°25′ South Latitude and 19°1′ East Longitude from Greenwich, which nearly agrees with the observations made at the Cape Town by Messrs. Mason and Dixon in 1761." This startling reference to "our own" Mason and Dixon is a reminder that before these two English astronomers were employed in surveying the boundary between Maryland and Pennsylvania, in the mid-1760s, they had jointly observed the transit of Venus at Cape Town in 1761.

Cook was not home again in England till July 12, 1771. In the three years of the *Endeavour's* voyage, thirty men had died of malaria and eight of other causes—but not one from scurvy. This was a remarkable record; in those days, scurvy usually took the lives of at least one third of the men on any long voyage.

The astronomical work had been well handled; its ultimate value suffered from an observational flaw that the planners had not foreseen. But Cook's greatest triumphs had been the drawing of extremely accurate charts of vast areas of the South Pacific and the adding of Australia and New Zealand to the British Empire. He had also enabled map makers to show vast stretches of ocean in places where the mysterious Great Southern Continent had been thought to exist.

Although Captain Cook had begun his voyage searching for information about non-living things—islands, a continent, the Solar System—he ended it by discovering wholly unforeseen aspects of the living world—coral reefs, kangaroos, and the strange world of the Maori tribesmen. It was these new realms of the living world that were to be among the great objects of study of generations that followed him.

GALAPAGOS ISLANDS

FERNANDINA

SANTIAGO

BALTRA

SOUTH PLAZA

SANTA CRUZ   BARRINGTON

GALAPAGOS
ISLANDS

SOUTH
AMERICA

The Case of the Vanishing Iguanas

Herndon G. Dowling

In the sixteenth century, Spanish explorers discovered a group of rocky islands six hundred miles off the western coast of South America. They found many unusual animals, including giant tortoises and lizards. Since the Spanish word for tortoise is galápago, the islands were named the Galápagos Islands.

The animal in the photograph is a land iguana, one of three kinds of large lizards that have lived on the Galápagos for thousands of years. There are no other lizards quite like them anywhere else in the world.

No one knows just how these animals reached the Galápagos. One theory is that, long ago, some iguanas were swept from the South American mainland and carried west by the Humboldt Current to the Galápagos. These iguanas gradually changed through the years.

Today one species—the marine iguana—lives along the islands' shores and feeds on seaweed. The other iguanas lived inland and feed on cactus and other plants. One kind of land iguana lives only on Barrington Island.

Recently, scientists have become concerned about the unusual animals of the Galápagos. Some species have died out and others seem to be vanishing. This story describes how a lone scientist has tried to solve this problem.

Imagine a rugged, volcanic island rising out of the sea. It is covered with thorny bushes and cactus. Peering out from the rocks are some lizards—four feet long, with scaly skins, spiny backs, and knobby heads.

This scene is not from the Age of Reptiles, millions of years ago. It can be seen today in the Galápagos Islands, which are six hundred miles off the west coast of South America. The lizards are called *iguanas* and have fascinated explorers and scientists ever since the Galápagos were first visited by Europeans in 1535.

Although there are about twenty kinds, or *species,* of the large lizards called iguanas, none of the others is quite like the three species living in the Galápagos. One of these, the dark marine iguana, lives along the rocky shore and feeds on seaweed. It has a flattened tail for propelling itself through the water. The other two species, called land iguanas, live inland and eat cactus and other plants. They have stout, round tails and are usually a tan color.

In 1962, I led a party of scientists and spent two months in the Galápagos studying the unusual animals that live there. Each of us had our particular interest—I studied marine iguanas, another scientist studied the giant Galápagos tortoises, and so on. However, we all became interested in the land iguanas.

The land iguana

These animals have disappeared from Santiago and Baltra islands and have almost vanished from Santa Cruz Island. Why are they dying out? This was the problem that concerned us.

For many years humans have been blamed for the disappearance of the land iguanas. Sailing ships used to stop at the Galápagos to catch these reptiles for food. The tails of land iguanas are considered a delicacy.

During the 1700s, sailors from whaling ships also killed the land iguanas for food. So did the early colonists who settled on the islands. Thousands of iguanas were killed. However, as far as we can tell, humans have not wiped out a single iguana colony.

Santiago Island is a good example. Sailors hunted iguanas there for many years. Still, when Charles Darwin visited Santiago in 1835, he found a great many iguanas. There were so many that "...we could not for some time find a spot free from their burrows on which to pitch our single tent," he wrote in his diary. Yet, a few years later the iguanas of Santiago vanished completely.

The Galápagos Island mail boat from Guayaquil, Ecuador, left us at the settlement on Santa Cruz Island in early March 1962. A few days later we set out to visit two islands where land iguanas were still plentiful. First we headed for tiny South Plaza Island. We traveled in the fishing boat of Karl Angermeyer, a Galápagos resident for twenty-five years.

South Plaza is a few hundred yards off the coast of Santa Cruz Island. It is only about six hundred yards long and one hundred to two hundred yards wide. As we explored the island, we found a small but thriving iguana population. Several adult lizards sprawled in the shade or basked on top of rocks. There were also many young iguanas. The young ones behaved differently from the adults. They hid in briar tangles or alongside fallen cactus stems. None of the adults seemed very large. I asked Karl about this.

"When my brothers and I first visited the island in the late 1930s," he said, the iguanas were as big here as elsewhere. Then, as more and more fishermen came to the Galápagos and stopped for a meal of iguana tail, the large adults disappeared. But the number of lizards has stayed about the same."

Next we visited Barrington Island, which is about five miles long and one or two miles wide. We went there on Miguel Castro's boat. He told us just where we could find the main iguana colony. Land iguanas were supposed to be common there, as they were on South Plaza. This was true, but what a difference?

The Barrington iguanas were all large, old adults. We saw about thirty adult iguanas—but not a single young one. (In 1964, a University of California field party saw three young ones and about forty adults.)

A population made up of adult animals alone cannot survive. I had a nagging thought about the Barrington Island iguanas. Could the same thing be happening here that led to the extinction of iguanas on Baltra Island? A United States military base was built on Baltra in 1941, and it was blamed for the iguanas' disappearance.

I began to reread a book by William Beebe, a famous naturalist who was head of the Tropical Research Department of the New York Zoological Society. The book is called *Galapagos: World's End*. I had skimmed several pages when I came to a sentence that had lingered faintly in my memory. It described the Baltra Island iguana colony of 1923. Beebe wrote, "Throughout all of our explorations of this colony I saw not a single lizard under 24 inches and most were three feet and even more in length." Baltra, then, had a dying population of land iguanas in 1923— long *before* the military base was built.

Why did the iguanas thrive on South Plaza, while they died out on Baltra and were vanishing on Barrington? Here was a real puzzle—but we had a clue. We had noticed one striking difference between South Plaza and the other islands.

The only kinds of large animals living on South Plaza were the reptiles that have lived there for thousands of years. Animal life on several of the other islands is quite different. Through the years, donkeys, goats, cattle, pigs, dogs, cats, rats, and mice have been brought to these islands by man. All of these animals roam about freely. We suspected that one of these animals, or perhaps a combination of them, was making life impossible for the iguanas.

We began to check the reports of other expeditions that had explored the Galápagos. We looked for two things: 1) What animals had been released on the islands; and 2) What was the condition of the iguana population?

We found that one large island—Fernandina—still has large colonies of land iguanas; and no other animals have been brought to the island by man. In this way it is like tiny South Plaza, which also has a thriving colony of iguanas.

The author examines a half-grown land iguana. He is trying to discover why these lizards are disappearing.

On all the other islands the iguana colonies were dying out or had already vanished. *On all of these islands there were other animals.* There were so many, in fact, on Santiago and Santa Cruz, for example, that we could not begin to say which kinds were responsible for the dying iguana colonies. However, on Baltra there are only goats, rats, and perhaps house mice. On Barrington there are only goats.

Soon we noticed something peculiar about every island where iguanas have vanished or are dying out. *Goats live on all of them.* Another bit of evidence—the first goats released in the Galápagos were put on Santiago Island in 1813. Santiago was also the first island to lose its iguanas.

We were convinced that goats were the guilty animals, but we were puzzled about how they caused the death of young iguanas. We noticed that the goats on Santiago and Barrington Islands had eaten nearly all the plants that they could reach. On Barrington the goats had cleared away all of the brushy undergrowth. They had also eaten so much of the larger trees, bushes, and cacti that the land looked trimmed and parklike.

However, the goats had not destroyed all of the cacti, which the iguanas eat. My first idea was that perhaps a combination of goats and rats were killing the iguanas. The rats ate the eggs of the iguanas when the rats' plant food became scarce. This might explain the situation on Santiago, which has both goats and rats. But there are only native rats on Barrington and they eat only plants.

This was the stage of my thoughts when I had to leave the Galápagos in 1962. Back in New York, my thoughts kept returning to the islands. I tried to think of some Galápagos animals that might attack young iguanas, especially if the lizards had no brush to hide in.

There are three good-sized, meat-eating, or *predatory*, birds in the Galápagos—lava gulls, short-eared owls, and Galápagos hawks. However, we had not heard of any reports of predatory birds feeding on young land iguanas. The young lizards are a

Goats roam freely on many of the Galápagos Islands. They have eaten most of the brush where young iguanas hide.

foot or more long. They seemed to be too big for a bird to carry away.

I returned to the Galápagos in January 1964. Then I found the last piece in my jigsaw puzzle.

Some scientists were camped on Fernandina Island, studying a colony of marine iguanas. One day, a Galápagos hawk swooped down and sat on a rock among the iguanas. Then it dived into a crevice and flew off with a young iguana. The lizard was about eighteen inches long! Later, when the scientists found the hawk's nest, they discovered the remains of several other young marine iguanas.

This was the first proof that the Galápagos hawk ate lizards.

With few hiding places, the young iguanas are easily caught by Galápagos hawks.

Moreover, it meant that these hawks could catch and carry lizards of the size of young land iguanas. Hawks are common on Barrington Island, where the young iguanas have few places to hide. I am convinced that a combination of goats and hawks is the answer to the disappearance of land iguanas.

This idea, of course, is only a theory until it can be checked by an actual food study of the hawks on Barrington Island. I hope that a biologist from the newly established Charles Darwin Research Station on Santa Cruz will be able to make this study. Meanwhile, however, it is clear that the goat—the only "foreign" animal on Barrington—is somehow involved in the disappearance of the native iguanas of that island. If the goats can be wiped out, perhaps the plants will grow back in time to give the iguanas a second chance.

The New York Zoological Society is determined to give the iguanas—and all the other native plants and animals of the Galápagos—a second chance. It has already given funds to the Darwin Station for the salary of a conservation officer. Miguel Castro, our knowledgeable guide, has been hired for this job. Already he has reported the results of his first project. Two hundred and ten goats were killed on Barrington Island in a four-day hunt! Less than a hundred remain, and he hopes to rid the island of them soon. Then the plants can grow again. We hope the young iguanas will grow, too.

Any new animal coming into a community of plants and animals that have lived together for a long period of time usually affects all of the plants and animals in some way. The situation on Barrington Island is the simplest case—a single animal was introduced into a small island community. Even so, it was difficult to discover just how the goats could cause the extinction of the iguanas. This is what makes *ecology*, the study of communities of plants and animals, one of the most difficult and one of the most fascinating of the fields of science.

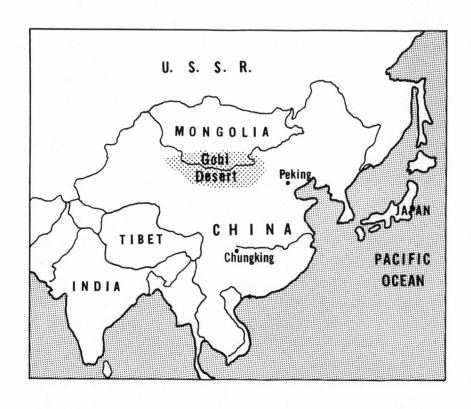

Expedition to the Gobi

Roy Chapman Andrews

One of the greatest of all explorers and naturalists was Dr. Roy Chapman Andrews. It has been said of Dr. Andrews that he combined rare scientific ability with the showmanship necessary to obtain financial support for his projects. As you might expect, an expedition to central Asia with forty men, eight cars, and 150 camels was a costly affair. Careful planning and much money is necessary to set off on such an expedition.

It was Dr. Andrews' life work to explore unknown regions in an effort to expand man's understanding of his world. To explain the significance of his discoveries and to get support for his work, Dr. Andrews constantly wrote and lectured about his explorations. This selection is adapted from his book All about Dinosaurs.

The Gobi, Asia's greatest desert, stretches two thousand miles east and west through the center of Mongolia. It is a thirsty land, bitterly cold in winter, burning hot in summer. A gravel desert with only sagebrush, clumps of wirelike grass, and thorny bushes. Gazelles, wild asses, wolves range the marching sands.

Until about forty-five years ago people knew very little about the fossil history of Central Asia. I thought that Asia might be the place where the ancestors of many of the animals of Europe and America had lived. So, in 1922, I gathered an expedition for The American Museum of Natural History. We wanted to search the Gobi for fossils and living birds, animals, and plants, and to map the country.

From a town about one hundred miles north of Peking, China, I set out with forty men, eight cars, and 150 camels. After three days we came to a bare gravel bluff on the edge of a wide basin. The *paleontologists* (scientists who study past life on earth) in our group stopped to look for fossils. I went on with the others to make camp. At sunset the paleontologists' cars came roaring into camp. Dr. Walter Granger pulled some pieces of fossil bone out of his pockets and his shirt. "These are the first fossils ever found on the Mongolian plateau," he said.

That evening Dr. Granger found many more fossil bone fragments around the camp. But we weren't sure what animals they were from. Next day, when we found a whole bone that was surely dinosaur, we felt like prospectors who had struck a rich gold mine.

On the second morning, searching alone about a half mile from camp, I saw many fragments of what had been big bones. Wind and frost had worn away the rock they were buried in and had broken up the bones.

At last my eyes caught the glint of a piece about five inches long sticking out of the sand. When I pushed it with my foot, it didn't move. I tried to pull it out. No use. The bone was solid in the rock. I hurried back to camp for help.

Dr. Granger and his assistant set to work with whisk brooms, small brushes, and chisels to remove the top covering. There, only a foot or two beneath the surface, was a great mass of bones. It was surely dinosaur! A new kind of dinosaur!

For a month the expedition worked in this one spot and even then did not take out all the fossils. We would uncover the end of a leg bone, only to find that it ran under another bone, which must be removed before the first could be touched.

More than eighty million years ago, in the Age of Reptiles, this area had been a great lake. When the dinosaurs died, their bodies must have been carried into a whirlpool in the lake. The bones sank into soft mud, and after many, many years they were *petrified,* or changed to stone.

About eighty million years ago, this country was warm and rainy. A thick jungle of palm and trees and other tropical plants rolled away in waves of green. Countless dinosaurs. swarmed over the land and splashed in the waters of the lake. Today only wolves, white-tailed gazelles, and Mongol tribesmen on horses trot across the plains.

We moved deeper into the Gobi. Sometimes we sat huddled in the tents for hours while sandstorms raged. After some weeks, we were far out in the waterless desert. But the weather was getting colder. Sometimes a light snow powdered the ground. If we

The author examines dinosaur eggs found by an expedition he led in Mongolia in 1925 for The American Museum of Natural History. Dr. Andrews was Director of the Museum for eight years. He died in 1960.

were caught by a blizzard, we might never be able to get out.

We started back. Our water bags were almost dry, and for one hundred miles there had been no sign of water. We were thirsty, but every drop had to go into the cars. On the third day, an hour before sunset, I saw far away a tent—the kind used by the Mongol people who live in the desert. Where there were people, there must be water!

We camped there that night, among beautiful stone mounds and cliffs that looked like animals or old castles. The setting sun made the rocks look on fire. We named the place the "Flaming Cliffs."

One of the men found a skull of a new kind of dinosaur lying on the ground. Bits of white bones were everywhere. Parts of skeletons were sticking out of the rock. There wasn't time to take them out, because night was on us.

In the morning it was hard to leave such a wonderful place, but the feel of snow was in the air. We might be trapped if we waited one day more, so we pushed ahead. Two days later the heavy snow came. By then we had reached the main trail and were safe.

The skull we had found on the ground turned out to be from a dinosaur that was the ancestor of a big American plant-eating dinosaur called *Triceratops,* which means "three-horned." The new animal was later named *Protoceratops* (first horned) *andrewsi,* in honor of my expedition.

The next summer we went back to the Flaming Cliffs. We decided that I would go ahead to the cliffs with part of the expedition. The slower camel train, led by a Mongol named Merin,

At the Flaming Cliffs, surrounded by miles of hot, dry desert, scientists spent months searching through sand, gravel, and rock for fossils.

would come later. We knew some of the camels would die from the hard work of carrying supplies across the hot, dry desert.

At the Flaming Cliffs we collected many fossils. Most of them were Protoceratops, but there were two or three kinds of small, meat-eating dinosaurs, too. We also found parts of a crocodile. That shows there must have been a stream or small lake in the basin at some time.

Though we were having great success, I was worried. Food was low, and Merin had not arrived with our supplies. I sent Mongols on horseback to search for the camels, but they found nothing. Luckily, hundreds of gazelles lived on the plains not far from Flaming Cliffs. From horseback I killed three or four a day for food.

Only two sacks of flour were left. We needed flour to make paste for removing fossils. When that was gone, work must stop. I asked the men what we should do. As food, the flour would last only a few days. As paste, it would be enough to take out many bones. Everyone voted to use the flour for work.

A few days later, one of Merin's Mongols rode into camp. Soon after, the camel train arrived. Many of the camels had died, but thirty had come through, weak and thin, carrying food and gasoline.

Until we went to the Gobi, no one knew how dinosaurs produced their young. It was supposed that they laid eggs, because dinosaurs were reptiles and most reptiles lay eggs. Still, no dinosaur eggs had been found.

On our second day at the Flaming Cliffs, George Olsen found three objects that looked like huge eggs. They were eight inches long and pointed at both ends. When we picked them up they felt heavy. The inside was solid red sandstone. The shell was broken, but it looked just like regular eggshell, only thicker. We thought they were dinosaur eggs. We had absolute proof later when a large rock was chipped open and we found two eggs that had unhatched baby dinosaurs inside them.

Under the sand near the eggs Dr. Granger found the skeleton

This nest with eighteen Protoceratops eggs in it was found at the Flaming Cliffs.

of a small dinosaur. It was only about two feet long and had no teeth. It was later identified as a new kind of dinosaur and was named *oviraptor*, meaning "the egg stealer." We think it had lived by sucking the eggs of other dinosaurs. Perhaps it was digging up these eggs when a sudden windstorm buried it.

Conditions have to be exactly right to preserve such delicate things as eggs. The desert was an especially good place. We think that the female dinosaur laid their eggs in shallow holes, then covered them with sand. The sand had to be loose so air and the sun's heat could get to the eggs. The unhatched dinosaurs got air through the shell, as birds do.

A model shows how scientists think Protoceratops dinosaurs may have looked as they hatched from eggs.

Probably during a windstorm, many feet of sand were heaped over some of the nests. This cut off warmth and air. The eggs never hatched. As more and more sand piled up, it became heavy enough crack the eggs, and the liquid inside ran out. At the same time, sand sifted into the shells and filled them up. This kept the eggs from being crushed out of shape. After many thousands of years the sand over the eggs was pressed together into rock.

Besides Protoceratops and fossil eggs, we also found the remains of mammals that had lived at the time of the dinosaurs. The Flaming Cliffs of the Gobi proved to be one of the most important discoveries of fossils in the world.

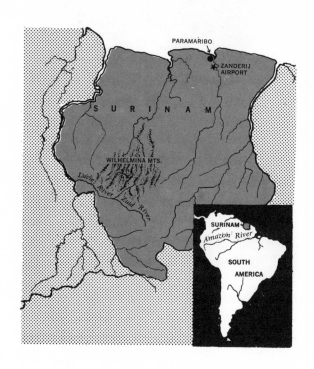

Exploring in the Rain Forest

Howard S. Irwin

Any expedition has many faces. Dr. Irwin and scientists from The New York Botanical Garden visit Surinam for numerous reasons. After careful planning so that several outcomes could be achieved by the trip, they collected over twenty thousand specimens. Other botanists will work for many years studying results of this expedition!

As our jet dropped down below the billowing clouds my pulse quickened a little. We were about to land at Zanderij Airport in Surinam (a self-governing Dutch territory in northeastern South America) to begin an expedition to a little-known mountain range.

While the plane circled the field, my thoughts wandered. I recalled the feverish preparations during the past few months back in New York and the thought of the adventure that lay before us. The plane trip from New York seemed somewhat like the "eye" of a hurricane—a brief calm between two periods of fast-paced activity. Basic questions came to mind. What brought us to Surinam? What were we going to do? Who would benefit?

If you stop a moment and think of what has happened to our North American forests in the last two hundred years, you will have one answer to the first question. As settlers spread westward and the population grew, the needs for living space and forest products increased rapidly. In time it became necessary to buy pulpwood and certain timbers from other countries. The demand for wood still increases, and now eyes are turned southward, to the great tropical forests in Central and South America.

The leaders of the countries of the Guiana-Amazon area hope that this story will not be repeated in their forests. But before

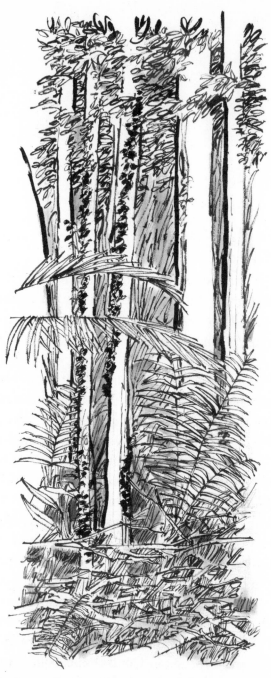

In the Surinam rain forest, palms, small shrubs, ferns, and young trees grow in the shade of slender trees that tower one hundred feet or more above the ground.

they can manage their forests wisely, there are some big questions to be answered. For example, what kind of trees make up this largest unbroken forested area in the world? Which kinds of trees are useful, or likely to be useful? The only practical way to answer these questions is to spot-check the forest in certain places, collect specimens from the trees, and take the specimens back to laboratories for study. Some of the trees may even be new to science.

This was one reason for our trip to Surinam. There were several others. As botanists we wanted to learn more about the kinds of plants and the places in which they grow. The only way to satisfy these interests was to go to the forests, study, observe, and take specimens.

Drug companies are interested in bulk collections of leaves, bark, seeds, and soil as sources of new medicines. Seed companies are always looking for new ornamental plants. Biochemists need leaves and flowers to study the types and make-up of plant colors, or *pigments*. Finally, wood specialists want blocks of wood to examine the structure and find possible uses.

Several years ago I had interested Dr. Thomas Soderstrom in going on one of these trips. He is a grass specialist at the Smithsonian Institution in Washington, D.C. Now at last, Tom was able to get away. To prepare for our expedition, careful plans had to be laid and many details worked out. One thought haunted us throughout this period: Despite radio contact with Paramaribo, the capital of Surinam, we would be on our own in the forest. Anything forgotten or overlooked we would have to do without.

To choose an area for our field work, we looked over specimen collections and read what scientists on other expeditions had written. At The New York Botanical Garden we have the world's largest collection of plant specimens from tropical America—a collection that numbers in the millions. Such a collection is called an *herbarium*. Each specimen in the herbarium is mounted on a large card which also bears a label that gives the botanical name, country of origin, date, collector's name, and so on. After working with these specimens for several years, I began to make a mental list of the places that were not represented in the collection.

Also, many botanists have published accounts of their own and others' expeditions, as well as of the new plant species that have been discovered on these trips. By plotting the paths of these past expeditions on a map, we got an idea of where the blanks were. This is how we were first led to the Wilhelmina Mountains of west-central Surinam. We were also attracted to the Wilhelminas because another New York Botanical Garden expedition went to a nearby Surinam mountain—called Tafelberg —twenty years ago and returned with some very unusual plants.

Our first step was to write to someone in Surinam who knew the history of field work in that country. Such a man was Dr. D. C. Geijskes, director of the Surinam Natural History Museum. Dr. Geijskes was born in the Netherlands but has lived and worked in Surinam for about twenty-five years. He replied that Dr. Gerold Stahel, a Dutch botanist, had climbed the Wilhelminas from the north in 1924. He reached the summit of Juliana Top, the highest point in Surinam. However, Dr. Stahel had lost nearly all of his specimens in a boat accident on his return trip. He had also abandoned a lot of equipment at his camp on Juliana Top. Dr. Geijskes hoped that we might find some trace of Dr. Stahel's expedition, something that could be brought back to the Surinam Museum.

This was valuable information. It told us that the Wilhelminas could be approached from the north. It also told us that someone had been able to reach this difficult area forty years ago, without the mechanical and medicinal aids we have today. We decided to go ahead with our plans.

Our next step was to get in touch with someone in Surinam who would want to join the expedition and who could, in the early stages, act as our agent for buying food and other supplies. He would also hire the field men who would cut trails and carry supplies and equipment during the three-month trip. We wrote to Dr.

1.

2.

3.

To prepare for the expedition, Dr. Irwin studied the plant collection to find unexplored areas (1), plotted his route on a map (2), and packed axes, twine, and one and a half tons of other equipment (3).

Jop Schulz of the Surinam Forest Department. He said that he and another scientist from the Geology Department would be glad to work with us. He suggested that we set July 1 as a target date because the dry season would begin at the end of that month. The beginning of the dry season is best for collecting plants. First, the weather is good, but more important, most of the trees come into flower then. The flowers are important for the identification of most plants.

Before going further we had to consider how our supplies and equipment would be carried from the port of Paramaribo to the Wilhelminas. There are no roads into that part of Surinam, and to ferry everything by river, as Stahel had, would take too much time. Dr. Schulz wrote that the Surinam government had recently built an airstrip on the Zuid River. The Zuid is a tributary of the Lucie River, and the Lucie flows through the Wilhelminas. We had our answer. We would fly everything in from Paramaribo to the airstrip, then use dugout canoes to reach the Wilhelminas.

Choice of expedition equipment is never easy. We always have to ask ourselves: Is it really needed? Is it portable? In this case another question would have to be asked: Can it be shipped by air? Often the answers are not simple. For example, since we cut many trees on these expeditions I have often thought of buying a motor-driven chain saw to replace axes. However, our Surinam field men know no such machine, and a chain saw in unfamiliar hands can be dangerous.

Our expedition gear was divided into eight categories:

1. Motors and canoe equipment—outboard motors and parts, gasoline, oil, cans, funnels, calking, rope, nails, tools.
2. Camping equipment—tarps, hammocks, kerosene lamps, shovels, rope.
3. Collecting equipment—plant presses, straps, pruning shears, duffel bags, plastic sheeting, newspapers, kerosene stoves and parts, boxes, burlap bags.
4. Cooking equipment—pots, pans, utensils, soap.
5. Food—rice, beans, dried fruit, crackers, sugar, coffee, powdered milk, cereals, salt.

6. Medical equipment—snake -bite kits, insect repellents, penicillin, local anesthetic, sutures, bandages.

7. Hunting and fishing gear—shotguns, shells, fishing lines, hooks, nets.

8. Personal equipment—clothing, blankets, mosquito nets, toiletries.

We had to decide where to buy each item—in the United States or in Surinam? We decided that categories 1, 2, 3, and 6 would come almost entirely from the United States. Cooking equipment (4), food (5), and hunting and fishing gear (7) could be purchased inexpensively in Surinam.

We began looking over our old orders from previous expeditions, leafing through new catalogs, and window shopping in search of new and improved equipment, lower prices, or, hopefully, both. We placed our purchase orders about January 1, 1963, in the hope that everything would be on hand by February 15 and ready for shipment to Paramaribo by March 15. It may sound strange to work so far ahead, but in expedition work one day's delay in the arrival of vital equipment paralyzes everything. As things were received in New York they were crated and addressed.

Meanwhile, arrangements were made with a shipping line with service to Paramaribo. We were told that because the ships have many ports of call in the West Indies, we should allow six to eight weeks for delivery.

By mid-March everything was packed. Our two tons of equipment were ready to go. In Paramaribo, Dr. Schulz had arranged for everything to enter Surinam without customs duties. As the truck pulled away from The New York Botanical Garden and left for the docks, I felt relieved. However, I knew that we could not relax. There was still much to do before leaving in July.

In another letter to Dr. Schulz we enclosed our final food lists, based on a party of four botanists and fifteen field men. We had already arranged for passport renewals but now had to get entry permits, or visas, to Surinam from the Dutch Consulate. Air reservations were made. We had physical examinations and dental check-ups.

Gradually we got our clothes together—ordinary light-weight cotton work clothes, about four sets in all, with a mixture of long trousers and shorts, long-sleeved and short-sleeved shirts. For footwear we chose basketball shoes. Leather, once wet, dries very slowly in the humid atmosphere of Surinam and often turns green with mold.

Finally the day came for Tom and me to clean off our desks, say good-by, and board the plane. No two expeditions are ever alike; an entirely new experience lay ahead.

We were met at Zanderij Airport by Dr. Schulz and Gerard Wessels-Boer. Gerard, an expert on palms, looked a little embarrassed at our efforts at pronouncing his first name in Dutch. "My last name is no better," he explained. "It means weasel-farmer. Why don't you just call me W. B.?"

Dr. Schulz and W. B. drove Tom and me into Paramaribo. Bicycles and motor scooters darted among the cars and buses. Masses of bicycles were parked under airy new school buildings. Soon we pulled up in front of the Surinam Museum and were met by Dr. Geijskes. "Your things from New York are all here," he smiled. "I've arranged for a couple of planes to take you and all the men to the interior tomorrow. The equipment will follow the next day."

That afternoon we met John Nunes. Dr. Schulz had asked him to be the field foreman. Usually we like to deal directly with our field men, but in Surinam that is a problem. Our men were Djukas, descendants of freed slaves who live in settlements along some of the rivers. John assured us they would be the best field men we would ever see. "They love the forest, the rivers, the wildlife. It's all they know."

The problem was that the Djukas spoke neither English nor Dutch, but *Taki-taki,* a mixture of English, Dutch, French, and African. We knew only a few Dutch words and no Taki-taki at all. John Nunes spoke both, and English as well.

At the airport the next morning we met the fifteen Djukas. They were short, powerfully built, and gay in spirit and dress. They shook hands with Tom and me, then with arms folded across their barrel chests, looked at us as if to say, "Well, when do we start?"

In a few minutes two DC-3s taxied up. One plane would be for people, the other for the first load of our supplies. In five minutes we were in the air and began the bumpy one-hour trip to the Zuid River airstrip. The Djukas were right at home. John told us that they had flown several times before, mostly on his geological prospecting trips. Outside the window, twenty-five hundred feet below, a magnificent unbroken forest spread before us. It was laced with meandering rivers and was interrupted here and there by a few grassy plains, or *savannas*, and palm-fringed Indian clearings. In the distance we could see mountains.

John nudged me and pointed. "That's Tafelberg Mountain. Beyond it are the Wilhelminas." Our plane began to lose altitude. The airstrip came into view, at right angles to the nearby Zuid River. As the tires squealed on the packed sand of the airstrip we all sensed that the expedition was really under way.

Here we were, in a remote backland area, about to embark on a three-month job for which we had been preparing for over a year. What would it be like? What sort of place is the rain forest?

The tropical rain forest is often called a "jungle," a word I have never liked. It brings to mind pictures of trees seething with snakes, panthers crouching in the brush, centipedes crawling into boots, and explorers hacking their way through an endless tangle of greenery. This is an image given to us by many books and movies, radio and television programs. It is not an accurate picture of the rain forest.

The true rain forest is a very different sort of place. Most of the trees are slender, with moplike crowns crowded together forming a dense canopy. Beneath the trees the forest floor is carpeted with the tans and browns of many different kinds of fallen leaves. Here and there the ground is sprinkled with the yellows, reds, and purples of wilted flowers. The carpet of leaves is thin, easily scuffed away to show the common soil—white or brown sands, or reddish clays. There is no thick leaf mold, because decay is a very rapid process in the rain forest.

In the rain forest the annual rainfall is often over one hundred inches and sometimes over two hundred inches. It falls in brief torrential squalls. All-day drizzles are rare. The humidity on the forest floor is usually close to 100 per cent, while the temperature stays around 75 to 80 degrees F. The light is dim beneath the leafy canopy of trees, one hundred feet above.

Because of the dim light there is little underbrush. Tree seedlings grow here and there, while ferns, dwarf palms, and large-leaved creepers grow in small groups, mostly in the wetter spots. It is easy to walk through this kind of forest. A machete is needed only to cut an occasional vine or hanging branch. It is along the river banks that the bushes and vines form a curtainlike thicket down to the ground.

There are two ways to travel in the Surinam rain forest—by canoe or by foot. For long distances the round-bottomed, dugout canoe is best. Most of these canoes are built with one flat end, where an outboard motor can be attached. Our canoes were propelled by eighteen-horsepower motors. They weighed between one and one and half tons when we finished loading them.

For two days, our eight canoes floated down the Zuid River and the pushed up the Lucie. Although these rivers are broad, deep, and slow-moving in most places, there are stretches where the water is shallow and rushes over rocks. Sometimes these rapids were too difficult or dangerous to pass. Then we had to unload the canoes and pull them over or around. We depended on the Djuka boatmen on this water highway, and their skill soon set us at ease. Hardly a rock was touched.

Toward the end of the second day John and I scanned our map, and finding the mouth of a creek, decided that it would be a good place to camp. We tied up to a mass of vines hanging from the riverbank trees.

Then began the most remarkable display of teamwork that Tom and I had ever seen. John and the Djukas took up their machetes and axes and disappeared into the shadows. Amid the crackle of branches and crunch of leaves, the machetes began to ring as they cut through the vines and trees. Down tumbled the vines into the water. Trees began to topple. Within an hour a camp site was cleared. Within another, small trees were cut to various lengths and lashed together with tough vines to make frames for our 12 by 20-foot canvas sheets, or *tarpaulins*. The tarps were thrown over and tied. Meanwhile Tom and I unloaded the canoes and slung our hammocks and mosquito nets.

The next day two Djukas were left to finish the camp. The rest of us set off toward Juliana Top, the thirty-six-hundred-foot peak

Arriving in Surinam, scientists from The New York Botanical Garden set out by canoe to collect thousands of plant specimens in the wild Wilhelmina Mountains.

Camps like this one were set up as the expedition explored the dimly lit Surinam rain forest. The men slept in hammocks slung under canvas tents, and the Djuka field men caught fish and shot game for food.

of the range. We hiked quickly through the rain forest, slowing only when we waded across small streams and felled trees to bridge larger ones. At 3 P.M. we made another camp, smaller than the big river camp. Tom, W. B., Dr. Schulz, and I would stay in this area for the next few days while John and the rest went on to clear sites for other camps. It was time for us to begin our work in earnest.

Our job for the next three months was to collect specimens from as many different kinds of plants as we could find—trees, shrubs, vines, and low plants. We collected along rivers, on mountain slopes, around rock outcrops, and from mountain peaks.

Sometimes a Djuka had to climb to the top of a tree to collect some flowering branches. If the tree was too difficult to climb, we cut it down. Sometimes a cut tree did not fall, because its crown was tied to others by matted vines. Then as many as six or eight trunks had to be cut before the tree we wanted finally crashed down.

We looked up into the leafy patterns of the canopy, searching for the flowers and fruit that would help identify a tree. We also looked along the ground for telltale signs: a withered petal, a berry, a shiny seed. These were the clues. It was up to us to find them and know what they meant.

We collected ten specimens of each plant. One set was for The New York Botanical Garden's herbarium, and one was for the collection of the Surinam Forest Department. The remaining eight would be used to trade for specimens of other plants from other museums.

We had to keep in mind that eventually, back at the Botanical Garden, each of the plants we collected would be mounted on a piece of white poster board, $11\frac{1}{2}$ by $16\frac{1}{2}$ inches. If the plant was the size of a dandelion, we collected a whole plant or even several plants. For larger plants, we selected a leafy branch with flowers or fruit, preferably both, together with some bark. If the leaves were very large—like those of the banana plant—one leaf was cut into pieces and mounted on a series of cards. Fruits that do not dry well were preserved in alcohol or formaldehyde.

As the fresh plants were collected, we wrapped them in plastic sheeting and stuffed them into duffel bags. We also took notes on flower color, height of the plant, soil type, and anything else that the collected specimen did not show. Finally, we cut wood blocks from the trunks and filled burlap bags with leaves and bark from trees that might interest plant chemists. Usually we had all the specimens we could carry by midafternoon. Then we headed back to camp.

At camp we often took a dip in a nearby stream and changed into dry clothes. Then we began to put our specimens into drying presses while the Djukas set out with their shotguns and fishing tackle, hoping to bring in some game to brighten our rice-and-beans fare.

After we laid out the plastic-wrapped specimens and gave them collection numbers, we entered the same set of numbers in a field book, along with notes we had jotted down on paper while collecting the specimens. This information is important, since it will eventually go onto the specimen's label.

Each specimen was spread out on a half sheet of newspaper, which was then folded over and laid on top of a plant press. When the specimens piled up to about five feet high, we tied the press as tightly as possible and set it on a frame over a kerosene stove. Hot air from the stove passed through the press, carrying away the moisture from the specimens. They dried in about six to eight hours. Leaving them in their newspapers, we dusted them with DDT or naphthalene to keep out insects, tied them into bundles, and then packed them into boxes.

While we pressed the plants, the Djukas came back with their catch. It might be deer, bush pig, agouti, capybara, tapir, bush fowl, even alligator, or any of twenty or more different kinds of fish. The cook had the fire ready, and before long there was food bubbling and sizzling in half a dozen different pots and pans. The food was simple but always appetizing.

After coffee the presses were checked, stoves pumped, and plans laid for the next day. Then, after some talk or quiet reading, we turned in, usually by 9 P.M. We worked seven days a week, fourteen hours a day, but there was no complaining. We liked our work, and with our time being limited, there was nothing to do but get on with the job.

So the days passed. We moved up to another camp every few days. As we moved farther away from the Lucie River camp, more Djukas had to serve as load bearers. They took dried specimens back to the river camp and returned with food. Within a month we had reached Juliana Top. We made three separate trips to the summit but found no trace of the camp or equipment that was abandoned there by Dr. Gerold Stahel's 1924 expedition.

Each of the twenty thousand plant specimens collected was spread on a half sheet of newspaper. Then the sheet was folded over and pressed together with other specimens. The pressed plants were then set on a frame over a stove to dry.

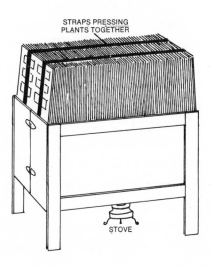

STRAPS PRESSING
PLANTS TOGETHER

STOVE

After working for a month on Juliana Top and nearby peaks, we began our slow retreat to the Lucie River camp. We cut wood blocks from many trees and collected specimens from trees that had come into flower since we had first passed through.

By early October we had hiked out of the forest and were again in our river camp. The river, which nearly overflowed its banks in July, was now fifteen feet lower. Many more rocks were exposed. The Djukas had to build a ladder down to the canoes. Within a few days we began taking our collections back to the airstrip. The radio operator at the airstrip alerted Dr. Geijskes in Paramaribo to send the planes. Tom and I were the last to leave the river camp. By now the water was so low that we had to jump into the river many times to help the canoes over rocks.

At the airstrip we said good-by to the Djukas. They were to return to Paramaribo first. By the time we arrived, they were off to join their families. In a few days Tom and I bid farewell to our Surinam friends and left for home. Another expedition had ended.

The end of an expedition marks the beginning of other work that may go on for many years. The blocks of wood that we collected are still being tested, and the test results may not be known for two or three years. Also, it is too early to know anything about the material that was collected for drug companies. Labels are still being prepared for the twenty thousand specimens that we collected. Once the plants are labeled, some will be sent to botanists who are interested in studying these particular kinds of plants. They will send back their findings in about six months' to two years' time.

Still other specimens will be exchanged with other botanical museums. After subtracting two thousand specimens for the New York herbarium and two thousand for the Surinam Forest Department, there will be sixteen thousand specimens left. These will be divided into twelve or fifteen sets and sent to other botanical museums throughout the world.

In this way, we will send the specimens from Surinam to plant scientists all over the world, and sixteen thousand different specimens will be returned to us in exchange. Our original 2,000 kinds of plants will swell to as many as twenty thousand different kinds for our collection.

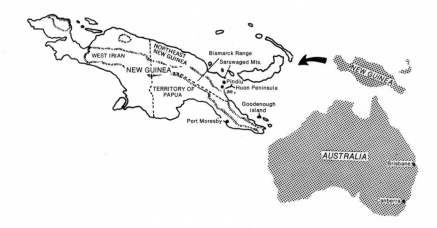

In the Land of the Bikpela Rat Moa

Hobart M. Van Deusen

A cyclone named Henrietta...a bush pilot looking for a tiny landing strip in a jumble of limestone ridges...swaying bamboo bridges stretched over mountain torrents...a meal of python steaks...and drums throbbing in the night! Does this sound like a James Bond adventure? Actually, it is simply a fairly normal chain of events in the lives of two mammal collectors in the tropics. Here, then, is the story of the American Museum's expedition in 1964 to the largest tropical island in the world—New Guinea.

The expedition had its beginning some time ago, in 1959. It was a beautiful late autumn day in June (the seasons are reversed in New Guinea, since it is below the equator). On that day, I stood on the peak of Mount Wilhelm, fifteen thousand feet above the north coast of New Guinea. I could look out across the valley formed by the Ramu and Markham rivers to the massive blue bulk of the high Saruwaged Mountains on the Huon Peninsula. We had been collecting mammals and studying plants for many weeks in the great chain of mountains that makes up the fifteen-hundred-mile-long backbone of New Guinea.

Right then and there I decided that if I ever returned to New Guinea, I would climb the remote peaks of the Saruwaged Mountains. I wondered what plants and animals lived there. I wanted to study the differences between the animal species we had collected in the Bismarck Range and those animals living in the mountains of the Huon Peninsula. Thus, in 1959 I began making plans for an expedition in 1964.

Choosing a team is the most important job in setting up any expedition, especially one that stays in the field for six months or more. Every man must know his job and be willing to work cheerfully under difficult conditions. A happy camp is just as important as a happy ship.

I asked Stanley Grierson, a naturalist and professional photographer, to help with the collecting and to make a photographic record of the trail and camp activities. As plant collector I chose a Dutch-born Australian botanist, Dr. R. D. Hoogland, who had done a great deal of plant exploring in New Guinea.

Any collector who ventures into the rugged mountains of New Guinea needs a pair of strong legs. Roads are very few and far between. New Guinea is dotted with small airstrips, but it often takes days of hard walking after leaving the airstrip to reach camp. All camping gear, tents, collecting supplies, and food must be back-packed over the slippery mountain trails.

These conditions make it very important to hire a dependable man to recruit people to carry our gear from one camp site to another, to bargain for native food supplies, to make and break camp, and to help with the collecting. In this case, such a man also had to be able to be understood by the people of the Huon Peninsula. New Guinea, because of its mountains and many isolated valleys, has an incredible number of local languages—nearly seven hundred at latest count! Fortunately, in almost every village of the Huon Peninsula, there is someone who knows how to speak the delightful "shorthand" language—Pidgin English. So my first requirement for an expedition "manager" was a man who could speak "pidgin."

Again I was fortunate. The wife of a coffee plantation owner wrote that her younger brother, Ken MacGowan, was looking for such a job. Ken was born in New Guinea and spoke fluent "pidgin." In addition, as I soon learned in the field, Ken was just as skilled at handling animals as he was at organizing camps and carrier lines.

Next, I had to find a dependable cook. Some say that a good cook is the most important person on an expedition! Fortunately, finding a cook was no problem. On three earlier trips our cook had been a man named Kim, a Papuan from Goodenough Island off the east end of New Guinea. Kim, an adventurer at heart and the best camp cook I have ever known, was delighted to join our

The author, Hobart Van Deusen (kneeling in foreground), is shown with other biologists from The American Museum of Natural History as they get equipment ready and pack it for an expedition to New Guinea.

expedition. Our roster was now complete except for some men to help Ru Hoogland collect plants and to help me collect mammals. These men would be hired later, when we reached the Huon Peninsula.

Early in the 1930s Richard Archbold, a Research Associate of The American Museum of Natural History in New York City, was looking over the world for a challenging area for biologists to explore. New Guinea was a natural choice. This tropical island had been discovered centuries earlier, but its rugged interior was still almost unknown. The island gave promise of having the richest plant life in the world. Also, birds of paradise, giant rats, and strange marsupials were known to live there. But next to nothing was known about their lives or exactly where they lived.

Archbold's interest in New Guinea led to three history-making expeditions during the 1930s. But then World War II interrupted. After the war, Dr. Leonard J. Bass, botanist on the Archbold Expeditions, organized a 1948 trip to northeastern Australia, and then he led expeditions to New Guinea in 1953, 1956, and 1959.

But why a seventh expedition to the *same* island? New Guinea is no "ordinary" island. It is over 315,000 square miles in area (more than Texas and New York combined). It is far more mountainous than California. On any one trip (even though it lasts a year) we can study carefully only a few square miles of country. To make each study worthwhile, we try to establish camps in several different kinds of country, or *habitats*—from low-lying coastal rain forest up through oak, beech, "mossy," and subalpine forests to alpine grasslands in the high mountains. As we go from one habitat to another, we find changes in the communities of plants and animals living in them.

There are many reasons for such studies. Man's curiosity knows no bounds. Scientists from places such as the American Museum extend this curiosity into the world about us. Science, after all, is simply organized curiosity. It is because of this desire to know our planet that we go on expeditions.

There are, however, other reasons for expeditions to remote areas like New Guinea. One reason is the study of diseases. The tiny parasites (such as lice, mites, ticks, and fleas) that live on animals may be carriers of disease. So we collect these parasites from the animals that we catch and preserve for the Museum's study collections. The parasites can then be studied by *medical entomologists*—scientists who study insects and other small animals that carry disease. In case of an outbreak of disease, their findings will help to identify the disease carriers.

Another practical reason for our expedition was to collect samples of plants that might be sources of medicines. We also collected

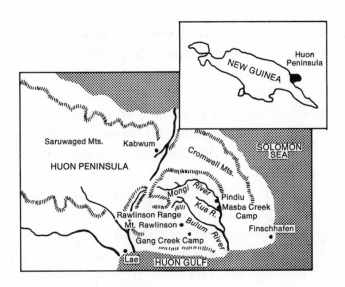

wood samples from trees. The tropical forests, with their many tree species, will one day supply a wood-hungry world with many useful woods. Even today some of the finest plywood ever made is exported from New Guinea.

Getting ready for an expedition, especially mammal collecting, is an easy matter. No two expeditions are ever the same, but you simply have to remember that the equipment should be kept to the essentials ("What do I really need?"), and it should be light and easily carried. Everything is packed into plywood boxes with reinforced ends and canvas tops. Such boxes are ideal for storage and travel in the field. Into these boxes we put such things as tents, clothing, traps, and other collecting gear.

Our food supplies would be bought in New Guinea. Trading stores in the larger towns carry all the needed staples, such as rice, flour, salt, sugar, tea, canned corned beef, jam, and powdered milk and eggs. On the Huon Peninsula we were often able to buy fresh fruit and vegetables. The native women thought nothing of walking for several hours to sell us their loads of local foods.

Getting and packing supplies for plant-collecting was a more complicated matter. A botanist needs portable drying ovens, kerosene pressure lamps, drums of kerosene, plant presses, bales of newspapers, special blotting paper, straps, chemicals for preserving flowers, axes, saws, aluminum carrying-boxes, canvas bags, and many other items.

For actually getting the mammals, we needed traps of several kinds, bait (raisins, peanut butter, fat bacon, and rolled oats), mist nets (nets of fine silk or nylon mesh for collecting bats), shotguns, and ammunition.

To prepare and preserve the skins and skulls of the mammals we collected, we packed cotton, needles and thread, labels, chemicals, scalpels, scissors, drying boards, pins, and wire. We also had small bottles of alcohol for preserving parasites. Finally, we packed medical supplies, especially drugs to combat malaria.

Ru Hoogland shipped the plant-collecting gear from Canberra, Australia. We sent the remaining supplies by freighter in December 1963, from New York for the ten-thousand-mile trip to Brisbane, Australia. From there they would be shipped to Lae, New Guinea, which was to be our base. We planned to assemble in Lae in April 1964, buy our food supplies, and get our gear ready to be flown to the village of Pindiu in the heart of the Huon Peninsula.

Stan Grierson and I sailed from New York by freighter early in March. The only event that interrupted the long voyage across the Pacific was our meeting with cyclone Henrietta. It was the largest of all recorded cyclones off the eastern Australian coast. Our ship's captain decided to steam at full speed across the southerly course of the slowly advancing cyclone and run for the Queensland coast.

After three days of battering seas and shrill winds, we woke to the normal sounds of a ship at sea and the welcome sight of the Glasshouse Mountains that rise abruptly from the flat plains north of Brisbane. A few hours later we docked at our berth on the Brisbane River.

That night we flew north along the Barrier Reef and then over the Coral Sea, landing in Port Moresby, New Guinea, just at sunrise. After a day of making official calls, we flew over the Owen Stanley Range to Lae at the head of the Huon Gulf on the north coast of New Guinea. The long months of preparation were over, and we could see the high peaks of the Saruwageds looming behind Lae as our plane began to land.

Old friends, familiar sights—settling in at Lae had all the feeling of "coming home." The high humidity, the sudden showers, the smell of decaying vegetation mixed with the salt breezes off the Gulf, the nightly chorus of frogs in the Botanic Gardens, the geckos (a kind of lizard) on the ceiling chasing moths near every light—yes, I was surely in the tropics again!

We made headquarters for the expedition at the Herbarium and Botanic Gardens in Lae, New Guinea. While Ken MacGowan assembled our food supplies, Ru Hoogland, Stan Grierson, and I unpacked the crates and organized our gear. We arranged it in

Gecko lizard

loads of different weights. The load limit for one person was forty pounds.

We discovered that the New Guinea women are more used to carrying heavy loads than the men. The men seldom carry more than a spear or bow and arrows and a piece of sugar cane or sweet potato to eat along the trail. The women all have big string bags, called "bilums," made of plant fibers. In these bags the women carry all sorts of heavy loads, including drums of kerosene.

Soon it was time to leave for the mountains. The single-engined airplane seemed like a toy beside our pile of boxes and bags, but I was amazed to see how much gear could be "shoe-horned" into it. Small airplanes have opened a new era of travel in New Guinea. Dozens of tiny airstrips have been carved out of the mountains. Now, patrol posts that once took days of walking to reach are within an hour's flight. Flying over New Guinea's rugged terrain is so dangerous, however, that flight plans are strictly followed, the pilots must make frequent flight reports, and no craft is allowed in the air after dark.

We had decided to make the village of Pindiu our mountain air base. Located in the heart of the Huon Peninsula, Pindiu is the center of a network of footpaths leading to the three mountain ranges we would explore during the next six months.

I was on the last of the three flights needed to carry the expedition to Pindiu. Our pilot flew east along the south coast of the Huon Peninsula. This gave us a close-up view of the Rawlinson Range, whose south slopes drop sharply from the summits to the shores of the Huon Gulf. The dense forest on Mt. Rawlinson was unbroken by villages or garden plots and looked like a promising area to explore. Soon we saw the Mongi River and turned inland toward Pindiu. A few minutes later we landed on the Pindiu airstrip, a shaved-off top of a ridge between two small rivers, encircled by forested mountains.

We were met by a patrol officer and his wife who offered us a "grass house" that had been their home until a few months before. Our house had a thatched roof, and the outside walls were made of woven bamboo strips. One whole side was an open-air porch with a glorious view of the valleys and mountains. After moving in, we collected the snakes that lived in the roof of our home.

Pindiu was an ideal base and supply camp, but the area nearby was too disturbed by man to be good for our studies. Most of the forest had been cut down. We wanted to learn about the life of New Guinea's wild forests and grasslands. But Pindiu was valuable as a "shakedown" camp. We got to know each other and trained our crew in the work they would be doing for the next few months.

The mammals of New Guinea are most active at night. To collect bats, we set up mist nets, stretching them across paths and clearings where bats might fly. To collect other mammals, we set traps and also hiked the native trails at night, carrying a shotgun and wearing a hunting light (a flashlight head mounted on an elastic headband, powered by a battery pack that snaps onto the belt). As we walked slowly through the forest, we swung the beam from tree to tree, from branch to branch. Soon we saw the light

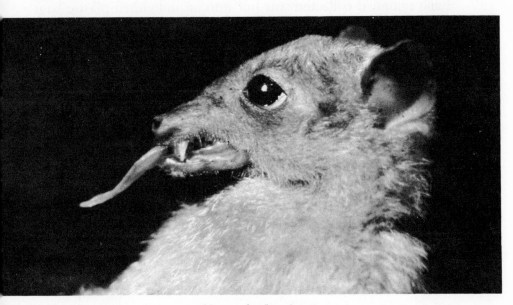

Nectar-feeding bat

reflected from the eyes of a tree-climbing mammal. It is not a sporting way to hunt, but we couldn't easily get many of the New Guinea mammals in other ways.

During an expedition we cover hundreds of miles of trails at night. It is a strange and exciting experience. Every sense is attuned to the surroundings. Sometimes roosting birds and hunting tree-snakes are caught in the beam of our head lamp. Small bats fly by on the trail. Overhead we hear the muffled swish of the soft wings of giant fruit bats.

We can hear the thud of fruits dropped by feeding bats, the chorus of frogs, leaves rustling on the forest floor, the calls of night birds. As the weeks pass, our ears gradually sort out these night sounds, but there are always some that remain a mystery.

At Pindiu and at our next camp at Masba Creek, we fell into the simple routines of a collecting camp. Each day we were up at daybreak to check our traps before the ants (many of which are active in daytime) nibbled at the trapped rodents and small marsupials. Then we removed bats that were caught in the mist nets and lowered the nets for the day, so that birds would not be caught. Each mammal collected was put into an individual plastic bag. Then wads of cotton soaked with ether were dropped into each bag to anesthetize the fleas, ticks, and other parasites.

After this was done, we had breakfast—homemade bread, jam, tea, sometimes curried corned beef on toast, possibly even the scrambled eggs of bush turkey.

After breakfast, we went to work at the "skinning table." Each mammal was weighed, measured, and given a label and a number. Information such as the animal's scientific name, number, weight, and measurements were recorded in two places—on the animal's label and in a special notebook. The parasites were collected and put into small bottles of alcohol (one bottle for each mammal specimen). Next each specimen was skinned and dusted with arsenic and alum powder (to preserve the skin). Then the skin was filled with cotton or *tow* (a fine hemp fiber), and sewed up and pinned out on a drying board.

The photo above shows the author (wearing head lamp) collecting scorpions in a cave near the coast of New Guinea. Fruit-eating bats, called flying foxes (left), were also found in this cave.

1.

Among the many unusual plants and animals the expedition found in New Guinea were: 1) huge acorns from oak trees (the photo shows their size compared with a nickel); 2) the cuscus, a tree-climbing marsupial about the size of a cat; 3) many kinds of bats; and 4) tree frogs.

2.

3.

4.

This work sometimes took most of the daylight hours, depending on the number of mammals collected the night before. Then the traps had to be rebaited, mist nets raised into position, and new trap lines put out. We wanted to be ready for the short twilight of the tropics, for in this brief period bats hunted insects in the camp clearing. We tried to shoot the bats as they twisted and turned against the darkening sky.

Then we had dinner, a welcome meal after a tiring day. One evening we had delicious "snake steaks"—cut from a twelve-foot-long python we had collected.

At nightfall or soon afterward the forest is alive with feeding rodents and marsupials. This is the time for hunting the trails with shotguns and lights. It was often 11 P.M. or later when we returned to camp, so we just had time to collect the insects that were attracted to the lights and to jot a few notes in our expedition diaries before falling into our sleeping bags.

After two weeks at the Masba Creek camp, we returned to Pindiu to reorganize our supplies. Ken MacGowan hired a carrier line to take us on the three-and-a-half-day journey to Mt. Rawlinson. It takes less than ten minutes to *fly* to Mt. Rawlinson from Pindiu; this may give you some idea of how tortuous the trail is. On the way to Mt. Rawlinson, we had to cross the Kua and the Bulum rivers on swaying bamboo bridges.

On the morning of the fourth day we made camp, forty-five hundred feet up on Mt. Rawlinson and high above a rushing mountain brook (called Gang Creek). Men with hunting dogs offered to help us collect tree-climbing kangaroos and forest wallabies. This was a stroke of good luck because these marsupials are difficult to hunt in the thick mountain forest. We also trapped bandicoots, several marsupial "rats," and some unusual hopping rodents. (A New Guinea boy taught us how to catch these rodents in traps baited with large beetles.)

On one of the rare days when the summit of Mt. Rawlinson was free of clouds, Tobram, my assistant, and I climbed the long easy ridge that leads to the forest-covered seventy-three-hundred-

At the camp on Masba Creek, the biologists collected a twelve-foot-long python (above). Kim, the camp cook (below), made a meal of the python after cutting it into "snake steaks."

foot summit of Mt. Rawlinson. According to our local guide we were the first "outsiders" to reach this peak. We saw many signs of *cassowaries,* which are large, flightless birds. They are so wary that in all my years in New Guinea I have never seen one in the wild.

The Gang Creek camp was a successful one, we returned to Pindiu with a feeling of solid accomplishment. Ru Hoogland then took a small carrier group and set off to make a camp near the high peaks of the Cromwell Mountains. MacGowan, Grierson, and I followed, and after five days of carrying we reached the camp. We were at the edge between forest and grassy plain, about seventy-eight hundred feet above sea level. I will always remember this camp for its giant rats and their fleas, and for the beautifully furred water rats that Stan Grierson discovered.

One night at dusk he was shooting bats near the Mongi River

where it ran in a series of quiet pools at the edge of the grassland. He noticed something break water in the nearest pool. As he watched, a water rat surfaced and then swam to the bottom of the pool. He fired the next time it came up for air, but unfortunately the rat drifted away just out of reach and was lost in the darkness downstream. Next evening we were better prepared, and by the end of the week we had collected several of these water rats. Only a few of these animals had ever been captured; in fact, they have no common name, but their scientific name is *Crossomys*. Never before had any biologist watched this animal alive, swimming and diving in its river habitat.

Ru Hoogland left to make camps in the subalpine and alpine zones of the Saruwaged Mountains. He was joined a week later by Ken MacGowan and by a botanist from Canberra, Australia. They explored the Saruwageds for several more weeks, collecting and studying the plants of the mountain peaks. Meanwhile, Stan Grierson and I hiked to the patrol post of Kabwum. From there we radioed for a charter plane to carry plant and mammal specimens back to Lae.

We had heard that there were caves at the east end of the Huon Peninsula. If the caves were there, we wanted to find out what kinds of bats lived in them. So Stan Grierson and I found a small ship bound for the coast near Finschhafen, and by the next morning we were staying in a small house on the shore of the Solomon Sea.

A man offered to guide us to a nearby cave that ran completely through a limestone ridge near the coast. He led the way down to the bed of a small stream that soon disappeared into the mouth of the water-worn cave. Several hundred feet into the cave, we came upon a high-ceilinged, dimly lit chamber. We surprised dozens of "flying foxes" (big, fruit-eating bats) that flew out the far entrance.

The flying foxes and other bats roosted in this cave, and we collected some of these mammals. We also photographed the other life of the cave—whip scorpions, cave crickets, fresh-water

This white-eared giant rat is held by Ken MacGowan, who was hired as "manager" of the expedition. In the Pidgin English language of New Guinea, giant rats are called "bikpela rat moa."

crabs, and even a young black-headed python that we saw crawling across the rough ceiling of one of the tunnels.

Word came of another cave a few miles down the coast. We waded through a sago-palm swamp, and after squeezing through a narrow entrance, we found a beautiful chamber, its ceiling covered with odd-shaped stalactites. There were even more bats here than in the first cave.

Our time in the field soon ran out. The "team" reassembled in Lae to pack all the specimens we had collected. The end of an expedition is only the beginning of further studies that may take years to complete. The specimens we collected are now being studied by many scientists in various parts of the world. This expedition has brought up one step closer to our main goal—to find out what kinds of plants and animals live in one of the strange corners of our world. But many questions remain unanswered. Will we return? Yes, as long as we have curiosity, we will always return!

About the Authors

RUTH MCMULLIN has been interested in science expeditions for many years. After graduating from Connecticut College in New London, she joined the staff of an aerospace magazine to do market research in the fields of aerospace exploration and aviation. She is now a science editor for a major New York publishing house and reads every issue of *Nature and Science* with lively interest.

Mrs. McMullin lives in New York City, only a block away from The American Museum of Natural History, the scene of many pleasurable hours. She enjoys making weekend expeditions with her husband to the country, where they keep a small sailboat and explore Gardiners Bay.

DR. ROY CHAPMAN ANDREWS, who led a great many large-scale expeditions to little-known corners of the world, began his work with The American Museum of Natural History scrubbing floors. He soon was permitted to study whales, and for six years he followed them through stormy seas gathering information about whales the world over.

Turning his attention next to land animals, Dr. Andrews led the Central Asiatic Expeditions of the American Museum to the Gobi. Dr. Andrews was the Director of the Museum from 1935 to 1941.

HERNDON DOWLING became interested in reptiles as a Boy Scout and became a Scout Camp Naturalist while in high school. He majored in biology at the University of Alabama, attended a Naturalist Training Camp (offered by the National Park Service) during the summer of his sophomore year, and held a job as Park Naturalist (Paris Mountain State Park, South Carolina) in the summer of his junior year. During this time Dr. Dowling had a living collection of two hundred snakes in his own back yard and acted as one of the exhibitors for the university snake exhibit at the State Fair.

Dr. Dowling became Curator of Reptiles at the New York Zoological Park (Bronx Zoo) in 1959 and left for a research position at The American Museum of Natural History in 1967. He has been on expeditions to study and collect reptiles to Antigua, Jamaica, Martinique, Saint Lucia, and Trinidad, in the West Indies, to Mexico and Ecuador, and twice to the Galápagos Islands (for a total of over three months) five hundred miles off the west coast of South America.

JEAN LE CORBEILLER, the author of "The Many Worlds of Captain Cook," is a science writer and editor with a particular interest in history. Although born in Paris, he is a Harvard graduate and has spent most of his professional life as a science editor in New York City. He has served on the editorial staffs of the American Meteorological Society, *Scientific American,* and McGraw-Hill and is now at work on a history of The American Museum of Natural History. He became interested in Captain Cook's first voyage while teaching a course in the history of science at the Julliard School of Music in New York City.

During the past fifteen years, HOWARD S. IRWIN, JR., has spent much of his time in the field. Dr. Irwin started his career after college as a teacher of botany and zoology in British Guiana (now Guyana). Since then, he has participated in expeditions to central Brazil, Mexico, the American Southwest, and Surinam. He has served as the leader of no less than six expeditions, and departed for another central Brazilian expedition in early 1969.

COLIN M. TURNBULL is Associate Curator of African Ethnology at The American Museum of Natural History in New York City. He was born in London and educated at Oxford, where he studied philosophy, politics, and later, anthropology. He made his first trip to Africa and first contact with the pygmies in 1951. He returned to the Congo in 1954 and again in 1957, living closely with the Mbuti pygmies. He has written *The Forest People, The Lonely African,* and *The Wayward Servants,* all drawn from three extended field trips to Africa. Most recently, Mr. Turnbull supervised the new Man in Africa Hall at The American Museum of Natural History.

HOBART M. VAN DEUSEN became interested in natural history at the age of five years, when his cousin took him on bird walks in Branch Brook Park in Newark. When Mr. Van Deusen was only ten years old, his father decided to work in Colombia, South America. For three years, he enjoyed having no school work and exploring South America with his parents.

Dr. Van Deusen has participated in many expeditions during his years as Assistant Curator of Mammalogy at The American Museum of Natural History. He is also much interested in the work of the Explorers Club, where he is chairman of the committee which helps support young men and women who wish to do beginning scientific field research in various parts of the world.

Credits

Index